Bradley Sowash

That's Jazz
book two
Digging Deeper

Contents

D1297879

ISBN 0-8497-9726-8

kjos Neil A. Kjos Music Company • Distributor

What is Jazz?

What comes to mind when you think of jazz? Do you think of the cheerful, toe-tapping sound of Dixieland music or the slow, sad feeling of the blues? Perhaps Latin styles come to mind or Big Band swing music? Jazz is all of these and more. Born in America, jazz blended African, Latin, and European influences and it continues to evolve into a broad range of styles played around the world.

For you, the student pianist, jazz offers wonderful opportunities for self-expression through improvisation. Did you know that you improvise every day whenever you have a conversation? When you meet someone, you use your knowledge of words and language to make up a greeting right on the spot. In music, to improvise is to go beyond the notes that are written on the page. You use your knowledge of rhythm and melody to enhance existing music, create new music, and play it the way *you* think it should sound.

Jazz is rhythmic, upbeat, laid back, bluesy, exciting and cool, and you're going to have a lot of fun playing it!

How to Use That's Jazz

✦ Although this book has been designed so that the songs can be studied in any order, serious jazz students should read and play through it sequentially. Together with the *Warm Up* and *Going Further* pages, each tune includes a methodical lesson process designed to move you deeper into the world of jazz. For this reason, master each lesson one at a time using the steps described below.

✦ Piano teachers searching for jazz music for study or recital will find a treasure trove of resources here. Select tunes as supplemental music to traditional piano methods either individually or successively. The *Warm Up* pages provide you with helpful lesson plans.

✦ At its most basic, this book is a collection of jazz tunes for performance. The tunes are organized by increasing difficulty so that it's easy for pianists to find selections to match their piano skills.

1. *Warm Up* Pages

Begin learning a new tune by reading and playing the examples on the *Warm Up* page. Step-by-step instructions, tips on how to play challenging passages and specific exercises are all included here. Read and play this page at the piano to gain a hands-on understanding of specific elements of the jazz style. When the *Warm Up* page is thoroughly understood and experienced at the piano, it's time to move on to the tune.

2. The Tunes

CD Demonstration Tracks—Listening to jazz is the best way to develop style. Listen to the demonstration tracks on the enclosed CD to get an idea of how each tune should sound. If your CD player has a left-right balance control, you can listen to each tune in three different ways: 1) Leave the balance control in the center to hear both the solo and duet parts; 2) Adjust the balance control so only the right channel is playing to hear the solo part only; 3) Adjust the balance control so only the left channel is playing to hear the duet part only.

Practice Suggestions—Begin by practicing each hand individually at a slow tempo. Increasing the tempo will come more easily when the individual parts are secure.

Enhanced Repeats—Jazz musicians often spontaneously enhance melodies by improvising variations. The written arrangements in this book emulate this practice. Therefore, look for differences such as altered rhythms or embellishments whenever a melody repeats near the end of a tune.

Duet Parts—Each tune in this book has an optional duet part. Although the solo parts are designed to sound complete without them, the duet parts enhance the tunes, making lessons or playing with friends more interesting and fun. Switching parts is a great way to better understand how the parts work together.

Steady Beat—The jazz tradition is steeped in rhythm. In jazz, maintaining an even pulse is far more important than playing all the right notes, so it's a good idea to practice with a metronome or drum machine accompaniment.

Chord Symbols—Jazz musicians often play from lead sheets that include only a written melody and chord symbols. Chord symbols are introduced in this collection to facilitate improvisation and harmonic analysis even though the chords are written out. See the Chord Glossary on page 47 for a list of chord symbols and their related chords.

3. *Going Further* Pages

Advanced jazz skills, improvisation challenges and suggestions as to how to personalize the tunes are all included on the *Going Further* pages. Take risks while exploring these concepts and avoid self-judgment since, at this stage, results are less important than the process of discovery.

Anatomy of a Jazz Chart

The information below explains some of the unique features of jazz charts (pieces).

Style Indication—describes the desired rhythmic feel or groove with particular regard to the timing of eighth notes, e.g., "Swing," "Latin," or "Rock."

Swing Equation—a reminder of how swing eighths should sound.

Chord Symbols—indicate harmony to aid improvisation. Chord symbols are placed over the top staff.

Rehearsal Number—aids in communicating with other musicians, e.g., "Start at measure 3."

Optional Duet Part—In this book, the duet part is an optional enhancement of the solo part. It is reduced in size to distinguish it from the solo part.

Jazz Piano Articulations

(notation)	short and separated
(notation)	hold full value
(notation)	loud, accented attack
(notation)	loud and short; accent and staccato combined
(notation)	first note longer and connected, second note staccato; sounds like "doo-wat"

Swing Eighths

The swing style is at the heart of jazz music. It is characterized by *swing eighths*, which are played in a lopsided, long-short, long-short pattern. Use the process below to help you understand the swing feel.

1. First, play these eighth notes straight, as written.

2. Now, try these triplets (not too fast).

3. Try it again with the first two notes of each triplet tied together. *Voila!* You just played swing eighths! The triplets in example 3 sound just like swing eighths. Also try singing along with your playing using the syllables "doo" and "ba."

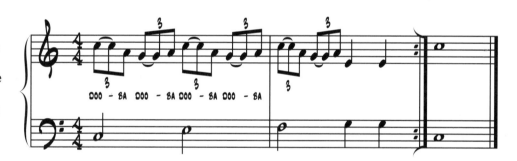

4. Most composers prefer to notate swing eighths as normal eighth notes. You will know to play swing eighth notes by the designation "Swing." You may also see this equation: ♫ = ♩♪ to remind you how swing eighths should sound.

Take It for Granite…Warm Up

Anticipation

When a note or chord that normally belongs on a heavy beat is played a little before the beat, it is called an *anticipation*. Because anticipations occur before they are expected, they add an element of surprise and energy to jazz composition.

1. To get the hang of anticipations, play these half note chords while tapping your foot on the heavy beats of the measure. Count out loud as you play.

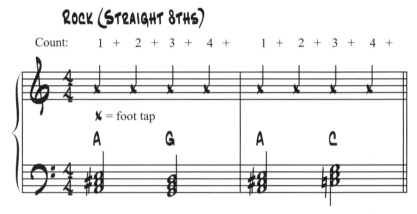

2. In this example, the final C chord falls *between* beats 2 and 3 (on the +, or "and," of 2). Play this example as you did before while tapping your foot and counting out loud. Play the C chord in the second bar after you say "2" but before you say "3".

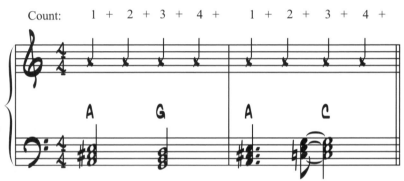

3. Try it with both hands in this longer example. The C chord in measure 2 sounds like it belongs on beat 3, but playing it early makes the music more exciting. The same goes for the G chord in measure 3. You can enhance this effect by playing the anticipations with more emphasis as is indicated by accent marks.

4. Add the melodic line to the left hand part you just learned, and you're rockin'!

Take It for Granite

(1)

Bradley Sowash

Take It for Granite...Going Further

Inversions

In **Take It for Granite**, all of the chords are in *root position* which means the note that matches the name of the chord is on the bottom. However, pianists often stack the notes of a chord in a different order so that there is a different note on the bottom. Chords rearranged in this way are called *inversions*, and many times they make it easier to move from one chord to the next.

1. Here are the first two chords of **Take It for Granite** in root position and *1st inversion*. Notice how the bottom note of root position moves to the top in first inversion. The chord symbol for the inverted chord is the chord name followed by a slash and the new bottom note.

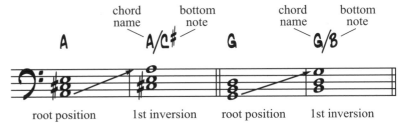

2. If you take a 1st inversion chord and move the bottom note to the top again, this new position is called *2nd inversion*.

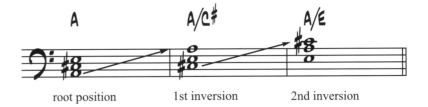

3. Here are the first few measures of **Take It for Granite** with some of the chords rearranged to be in first inversion. Notice how smoothly your left hand moves between these chords compared with the original version.

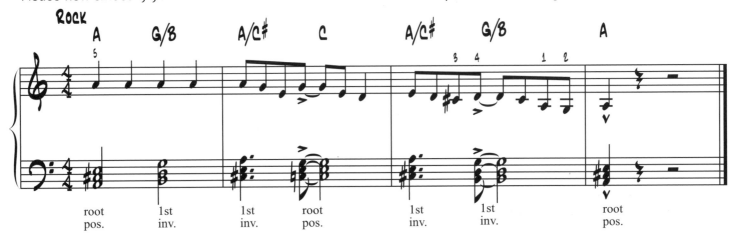

4. Here are the chords for measures 13-16 with the F chord in 2nd inversion for smoother left hand transitions.

Improv Challenge

Go back and play **Take It for Granite** using the chord inversions in the above examples or make up your own!

© **2006** La Jolla Music Company, Neil A. Kjos Music Company, Distributor, 4382 Jutland Drive, San Diego, California 92117.

Clave

Rhythms come and go but some of them are important enough to have earned their own names. **History of Flight** contains such a rhythm called *clave* (pronounced "claw-vay"), which is both the name of a specific rhythm and the instrument that most often plays it. The clave is the most important rhythm in Latin music. It's like a clock that holds the other rhythmic parts together.

1. Try clapping this basic clave. There are three notes in the first measure and two notes in the second measure. That's why it's called the *three-two clave*.

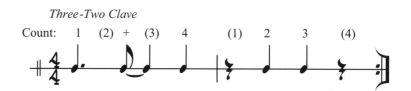

2. Here's another version of the clave in which the first and second measures are reversed. Since there are two notes in the first measure and three notes in the second measure, we call this a *two-three clave*. Clap the *two-three clave* until you are comfortable with it.

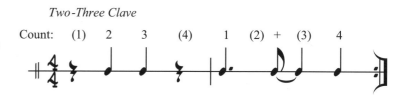

3. In **History of Flight**, the clave begins at measure 17. Play the left hand alone a few times. Why is there an F chord symbol when no chords are written? It's traditional to include chord symbols in jazz charts as an aid to improvisation and aid to musicians who "sit in" or play along.

4. Now add the right hand part. It also begins with the first half of a *three-two clave*. The next measure, however, has a different right hand rhythm while the left continues with the second half of the clave. Count out loud and use the lines to help sort out how the rhythms line up to the beat.

History of Flight

(2)

Bradley Sowash

History of Flight...Going Further

Improvising with Scales

When we practice scales, it is customary to begin on the first note and head directly up and down playing each note in order. However, in both written and improvised music, scales are rarely so orderly. For example, the C scale used throughout **History of Flight** moves forward and back in a herky-jerky fashion like an old airplane trying to get off the ground. Here's a neat way to practice improvising with scales that move randomly.

1. Begin by playing the C scale over these primary chords.

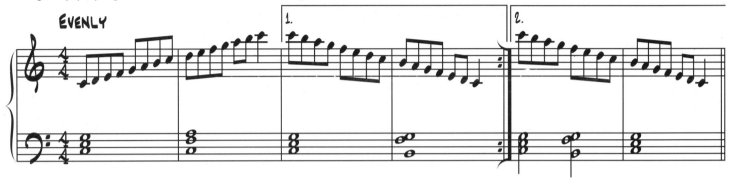

2. Now play the scale using continuous eighth notes and change direction wherever you like. Don't worry about how it sounds for now just keep changing directions. This example is just one possibility; your version should sound different.

3. This time, continue to change directions but add some longer notes into the scale wherever you like. The idea is to get used to the feeling of your right hand wandering about as your left hand plays chords. Your version should sound different than this example.

4. Finally, add some skips here and there as you play the scale, continue to change directions and use both long and short notes. Again, your version should sound different than this example.

Improv Challenge

Try this exercise with each new scale you learn using the primary chords that go with that key. It will enhance your ability to use your hands independently, help you hear how scales fit with chords and give you practice improvising.

Chord Shifts

In jazz, playing with a steady beat is very important. It matters even more than playing all the right notes. Yet, it can be a challenge not to pause when the chords change. Practicing *chord shifts* ahead of time will even out this common timing glitch, and help you play with solid time.

1. Play through the left hand chords from measures 5-6 of **Flint and Steel**. The second and fourth chord symbols (G/D) are *slash chords*. The G indicates the chord and the D specifies which note is on the bottom.

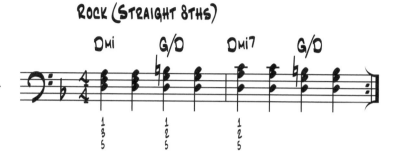

2. Measures 13-14 use the same left hand pattern but on different chords. The shift from measure 12 to measure 13 is one of those tricky places where it's easy to pause. The secret to doing it well is to quickly move your left hand pinky from D to G. Practice the four measures below until you can make the shift smoothly.

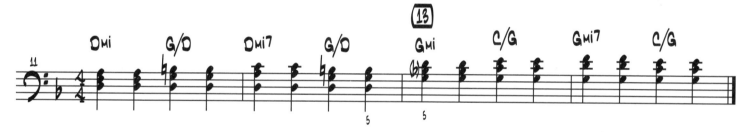

3. Another potential problem area occurs at measures 17 and 18. To help you negotiate these quick changes, use the suggested fingerings, or come up with your own.

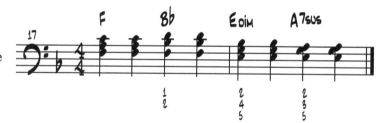

4. One more thing: Watch out for the left hand rhythm beginning in measure 21. It's different from what has come before (see example 1 above). Also, notice that the second measure is slightly different from the first.

Okay, you are ready to play **Flint and Steel**. Go light a fire!

Flint and Steel

Flint and Steel...Going Further

Improvising with the Dorian Scale

The idea of the Dorian scale goes all the way back to ancient Greece. In modern jazz, it is associated with "cool jazz" styles and remains a favorite tool among modern improvisers who appreciate the slightly altered sound it brings to the minor scale.

1. **Flint and Steel** is in the key of D minor. The scale associated with this key is the D natural minor scale. The scale steps (or degrees) are numbered in the following example.

D Natural Minor Scale

2. Another scale associated with D minor is the D *Dorian scale* (or mode). Compare it to the D natural minor scale above. In D Dorian the 6th scale degree is B natural, whereas in the D natural minor scale it is B♭. Because B natural is a half step higher than B♭, we say that the Dorian scale has a "raised 6th."

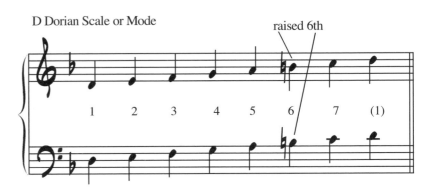

D Dorian Scale or Mode — raised 6th

3. What does all this Dorian business have to do with **Flint and Steel**? You can use the notes from the Dorian scale to create an improvised melody over the song! Play the following left hand part as a vamp (a continuously repeated one or two measure phrase), and improvise a solo in your right hand. (*Tip*: as a way to get started, choose three notes of the scale and improvise using only those notes, then choose four, then five, etc.)

4. The Dorian scale works for most of **Flint and Steel** because B naturals are used in the left hand. Notice however, that in measures 13-18, there are B♭s in the left hand. Therefore, switch to using notes of the D natural minor scale for your improvisation in these measures. Here's a sample solo to get you started. Pay attention to how the left hand part determines which scale is used.

Improv Challenge

Play the left hand of **Flint and Steel** and improvise a melody in the right hand. Use notes from the D Dorian scale in measures 1-12 and 19-28, and notes from the D natural minor scale in measures 13-18.

Get Up, Get Ready...Warm Up

Relating Parts

Jazz melodies (or right hand parts) often feature syncopated rhythms that fall between more straight-forward rhythms in the accompaniment (or left hand). When this happens, it is useful to notice how the melodic rhythms relate to the accompaniment rhythms as well as how they combine to make one overall part.

1. Start by playing and mastering the first few measures of **Get Up, Get Ready**, right hand alone. Don't forget to swing those eighth notes! (For more information on swing, see page 5.)

2. Now add this simplified left hand part. The lines help us see how the two parts line up. Notice, for example, how the tied D in the right hand falls between the notes E and F in the left hand.

3. Before continuing on piano, play this rhythm with your hands lightly tapping your knees. Your right hand taps the up stems and your left hand taps the down stems. Together, they make one part.

4. Now try adding the left hand "thumb" notes. Dotted lines will help with the trickiest rhythms.

Get Up, Get Ready
(🔘 4)

Bradley Sowash

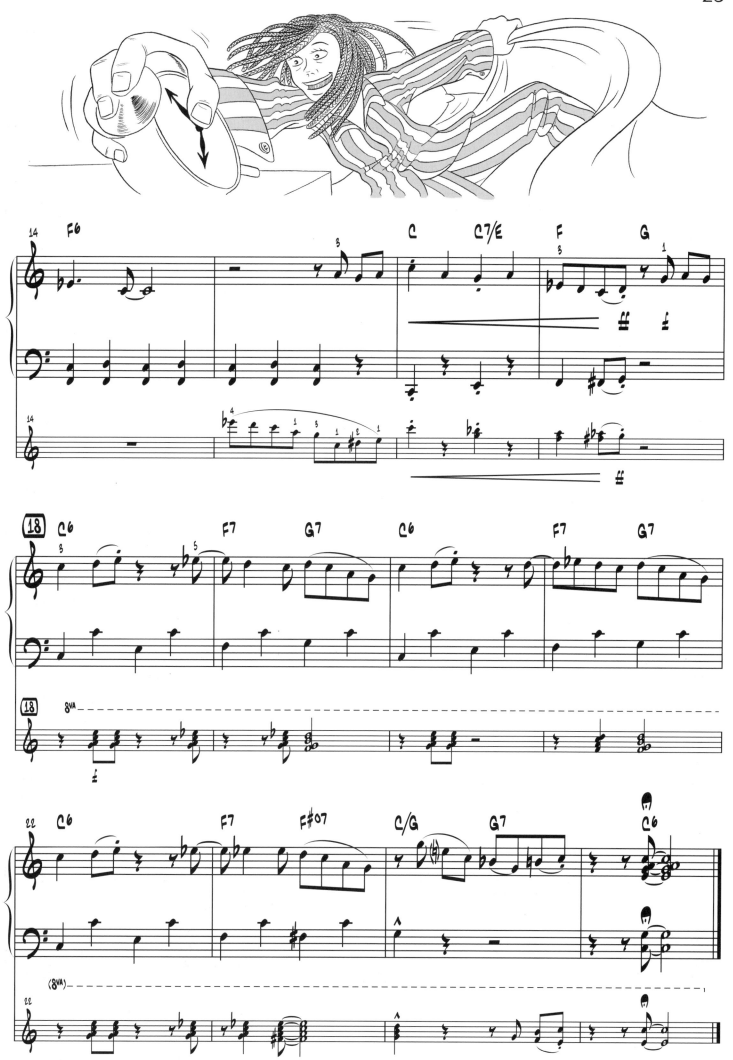

Get Up, Get Ready…Going Further

Improvising with the Pentatonic Scale

Jazz musicians love to play music not written on the page. They call this improvising, "ad libbing," or "blowing." You can experiment with this on **Get Up, Get Ready** by making up your own right hand part using the pentatonic scale. The *pentatonic scale* is a 5-step scale used by improvisers around the world because the notes sound good in many different musical settings.

The Pentatonic Scale in C.

1. Start by playing through the pentatonic scale in order. The notes of this scale work well together regardless of how you order them or even if you play them all at once (try it!).

2. Take the first three notes from the scale and improvise a melody over the left hand part. Then choose a different set of three notes and try it again. Keep improvising, each time using a different set of three notes, until you have used all of the notes in the scale.

3. Repeat the above exercises with four-note sets.

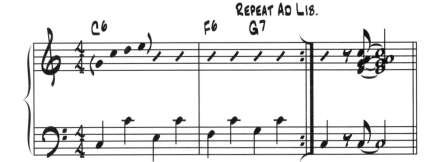

4. And finally, improvise using all five notes of the pentatonic scale.

5. Don't forget to use the scale in multiple octaves. Here are a few examples to get you started:

Improv Challenge

Improvise over **Get Up, Get Ready** using the pentatonic scale in your right hand to create new melodies. Play it as many times as you like, the more the better!

Piano as a Drum

Did you know the piano is classified as a *percussion* instrument? **Primal Beat** takes advantage of the piano's percussive nature with two-handed drumlike rhythms.

1. Here is the rhythm from the opening measures of **Primal Beat**. When the hands are working back and forth like this, it's a good idea to work out the rhythmic patterns before playing any notes. Play this pattern by tapping your knees. Tap the up stems with your right hand and the down stems with your left.

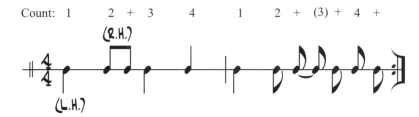

2. Now try the same rhythm on the piano. It looks a bit different because it is divided between two staves, but it really is the same rhythm as the previous example.

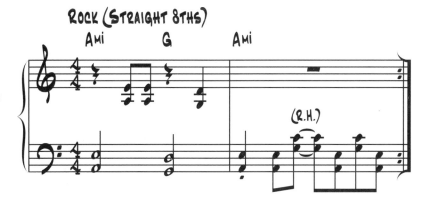

3. Here's a difficult rhythmic pattern found in measures 17-31. Again, tap the up stems with your right hand and the down stems with your left.

4. Here are the chords to measures 17-28 of **Primal Beat**. Practice them before going on. *Tip*: It's helpful to notice which notes stay the same between chords. For example, the notes D and F in the Dmi7 chord are repeated in the G7 chord. Find others and draw lines to connect them.

5. Now put it all together. Here are the same chords together with the rhythm you practiced in example 3. When you can play this, you'll be ready to learn **Primal Beat**.

Primal Beat

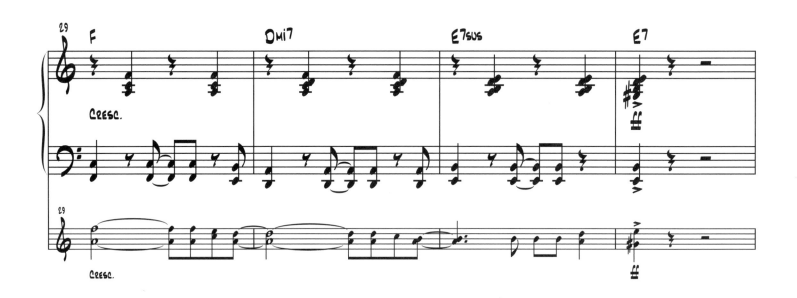

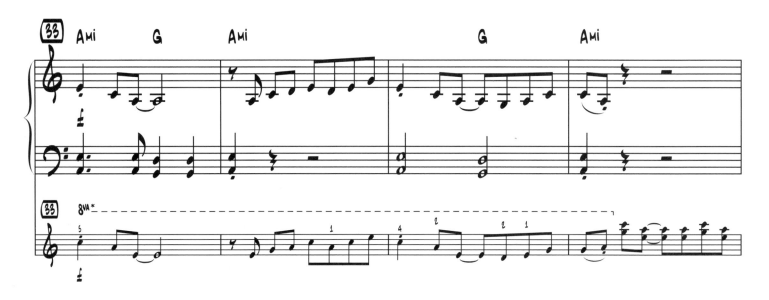

*8VA IS OPTIONAL FROM HERE TO ENDING.

Primal Beat...Going Further

Minor Pentatonic Scales

You've probably already discovered the versatility of the *pentatonic scale* as a collection of notes that works almost anywhere (see page 24.) These examples show you how to use it in a minor key.

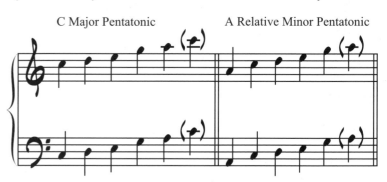

1. A pentatonic scale in a minor key has the same notes as the scale in its relative major key. Play through the C major and A minor pentatonic scales, and notice that both scales contain the same pitches even though they have different starting points.

2. Compare measures 5-8 of **Primal Beat** to the A minor pentatonic scale above. Notice that the right hand melody only uses notes from this scale.

3. Now, improvise a right hand melody using the A minor pentatonic scale.
   A) Begin by placing your hand in this position:
   B) Play the right hand as written to get started, then improvise a response in the bars with slashes. Improvise all four measures the second time through.

4. The A minor pentatonic scale can be played in any order. Improvise a right hand melody again with your hand in a different position.
   A) Place your hands in this new position:
   B) Again, play the right hand as written, and then improvise a response. Improvise all four measures the second time through. Start new patterns on different notes, and be inventive!

Improv Challenge

Go back and play measures 5-16 of **Primal Beat** with an improvised right hand part using the A minor pentatonic scale. Remember that the 5 notes of the minor pentatonic scale can be played anywhere on the piano in any order using any rhythm.

Counting

Math Whiz is aptly named because counting will make the rhythms much easier to play. It also involves addition and subtraction as explained in **Math Whiz** *Going Further*. For now, let's work on the counting.

1. Clap these rhythms while counting out loud. Say the rest counts (in parentheses) under your breath. Start with a slow tempo and maintain a steady beat. Practicing slowly will enable you to perform at a faster tempo sooner than if you try to stumble through too quickly.

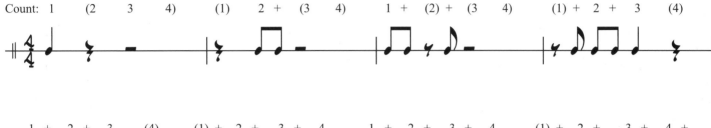

2. Below are the first eight measures of **Math Whiz**. First play the right hand alone using the fingerings given. Next, play the left hand alone. After you master the individual parts, put them together. Be as accurate as possible. Learning new music is like programming a computer: You've got to put good data into your hands and brain to get good results.

ROCK (STRAIGHT 8THS)

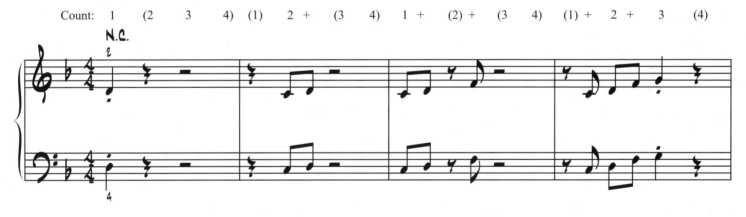

Math Whiz

Math Whiz...Going Further

Accumulation and Reduction

Accumulation and *reduction* simply means adding and subtracting. Let's take a look at how these concepts can be applied to music.

1. Accumulation means to add on. Consider this pattern: 1, 1-2, 1-2-3, 1-2-3-4…. Each new sequence adds a new entry while retaining the entries from the previous sequence. You could also do this with the alphabet (A, A-B, A-B-C, A-B-C-D…), candy (chocolate, chocolate-mint, chocolate-mint-gum…), or in music, as in this example.

2. Reduction does the same thing backwards by subtracting. For example, 1-2-3-4, 1-2-3, 1-2, 1. Each new sequence subtracts the last entry from the previous sequence.

3. In the beginning, **Math Whiz** uses accumulation by adding on notes in each new measure. Notice that the rhythm changes from measure to measure while the pattern grows.

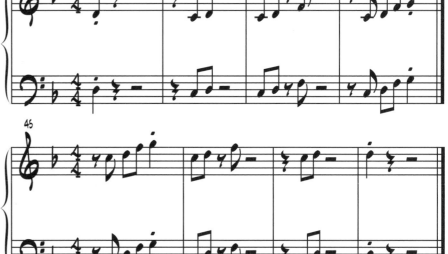

4. Beginning in measure 41, **Math Whiz** uses reduction by subtracting notes with each new measure.

Improv Challenge

Try making up your own musical accumulation using the chord progression below. You can do it in your head or you might find it useful to write notes in the blank spaces of the right hand staff to help you remember your ideas. When you've created a pattern to your liking, reverse it with reduction.

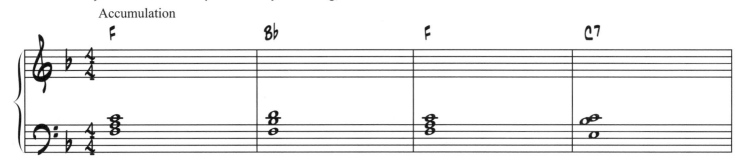

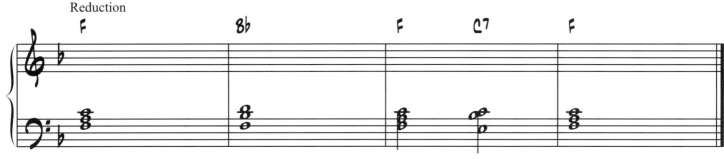

Blues Progression

Repeat After Me is in the form of a *12 bar blues*. This type of American music was introduced in the early 1900s and remains popular to this day. *Boogie Woogie* is a form of the blues that uses repeating left hand patterns to create an energetic accompaniment for right hand melodies and improvisations.

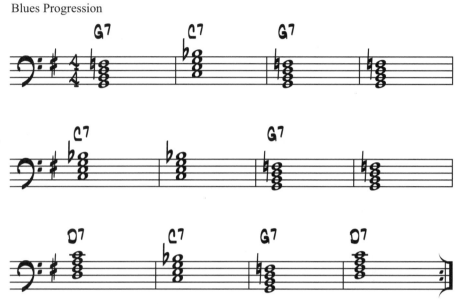

Blues Progression

1. The blues is a popular form of music that is generally twelve measures in length. It includes a specific set of chords called a *blues progression*. Play through this example of the classic 12 bar blues to get the sound of the blues progression into your ears and the feel into your hands. Every jazz musician is expected to be familiar with the blues, so it would be a good idea to memorize it now.

2. **Repeat After Me** uses a boogie left hand style. Practice this repeating pattern with just your left hand. Don't forget to swing those eighths!

3. Try holding down your left hand pinky so that it plays all the way through the measure as shown in this example. This will "anchor" your left hand making it easier to maintain the steady beat that is so important to the boogie-woogie style.

4. Long distances between left hand "anchor" notes can be challenging. Practice this example several times to become accustomed to this shift.

quick pinky shift

5. D7 is the last chord change. Even though it's not written this way, you should anchor your left hand pinky on the root note in this example and use this same technique all the way through this piece.

Repeat After Me
(♪ 7)

Bradley Sowash

Repeat After Me...Going Further

Bright Blues Scale

Blues is the most often used form in jazz, so understanding its associated scales is essential. The *bright blues scale* contains a *blue note*, which, like the spice in a great stew, will give your improvisations a characteristic bluesy flavor.

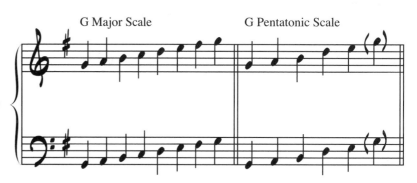

1. To review, here is the G major scale and the G pentatonic scale. The pentatonic scale is the same as the major scale except that it omits the 4th and 7th scale degrees.

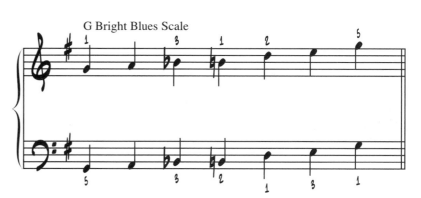

2. There are several blue notes but the most prominent is the flat third (B♭ in the key of G). Add the note B♭ to the G pentatonic scale and you get the bright blues scale. Practice the suggested fingering in each hand separately. (Don't worry about putting the hands together.) Next, try improvising with one hand at a time using this scale. Notice how the blue note B♭ adds just a touch of sadness to a basically cheerful sound. Like a piece of bad news on a good day, that's the blues!

3. Try improvising using the bright blues scale in the right hand. The left hand "walking bassline" is less difficult than the boogie pattern in **Repeat After Me** making it easier to think about what your right hand is playing. The small notes are written for reference only. You determine the order of the notes as well as the rhythm, duration, and octave.

4. Now try it a few times over a bassline that suggests a C7 chord.

© **2006 La Jolla Music Company**, Neil A. Kjos Music Company, Distributor, 4382 Jutland Drive, San Diego, California 92117.

Repeat After Me...Going Further, cont.

5. Now try it over a D7 bassline. Some of the notes in the bright blues scale seem to "clash" with this chord. However, the dissonance of these "off" sounding notes creates a bit of tension which is part of the character of the blues.

6. Here's the entire 12 bar blues with a walking bassline. Practice improvising using the bright blues scale in your right hand. The first few measures contain examples to get you started but you don't have to play what is written.

Tip: Try not to "fill up the measures." Rather, keep your improvisation tasty with sparse catchy rhythms using just a few notes at a time.

Improv Challenge

Now that you can improvise over this simple walking bassline, go back and improvise the right hand part to **Repeat After Me** using the busier left hand boogie pattern. The bright blues scale offers good note choices, but you are free to add any other notes that sound good to you.

Changing Feels

Jazz Musicians refer to the underlining rhythmic style of a tune as the *feel* or *groove*. Some songs require switching back and forth between two different rhythmic feels. **Farmer's Market** switches between Latin and Swing feels.

1. Practice this simple right hand melody, which has a "straight eighths" Latin feel.

2. Now try this similar melody with a swing feel. The first note of each eighth note group should be longer than the second. For more explanation on swing, see page 5.

3. To get the hang of *changing feels*, play through this exercise several times. The Latin eighth notes should be even and the Swing eighth notes have a lopsided long-short sound.

Common Tones

Common tones are notes shared by two chords. Changing from one chord to another is much easier when you pay attention to common tones between chords.

4. Here are the chords to the first eight measures of **Farmer's Market**. For each pair of chords, draw lines connecting common tones.

Farmer's Market

Bradley Sowash

Farmer's Market...Going Further

Enhanced Repeats

The form of **Farmer's Market** is AABA. With three A sections, it can get a little boring for the listener and musician alike. To counter this, jazz musicians instinctively *enhance* repeated sections to keep the song interesting and fresh.

1. It is customary in jazz to play the melody as written or "straight" the first time. After that, you are free to vary it any way you can. For example, you could change the rhythms in the left hand.

2. Another way to keep it sounding fresh is to embellish the melody through the use of repeated notes.

3. You could also add fills (shown here with small noteheads) in the spaces between the melody.

4. Here's a combination of all three.

Improv Challenge

Go back and play **Farmer's Market** adding your own variations each time the A section comes around. For a greater challenge, try doing it while playing the duet part instead of your left hand part.

Appendix A: Chord Glossary

Appendix B: Common Jazz Scales and Associated Chords

Major Scales

C Major

C Pentatonic (C Major minus the 4th and 7th)

omit   omit

C Bright Blues (Pentatonic plus flat 3rd)

flat 3rd

C Mixolydian or Dominant Scale
(C Major with flat seventh)

flat 7th

Minor Scales

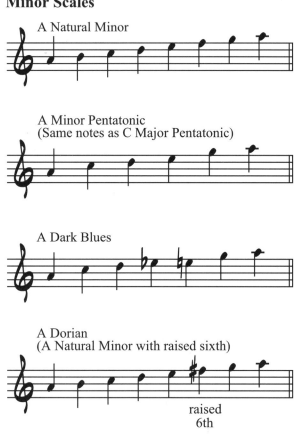

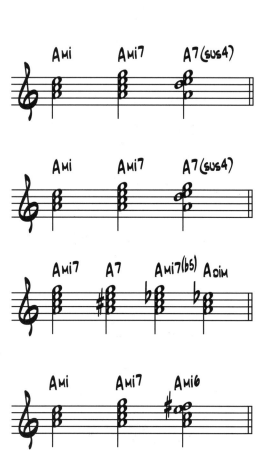

A Natural Minor

A Minor Pentatonic
(Same notes as C Major Pentatonic)

A Dark Blues

A Dorian
(A Natural Minor with raised sixth)

raised 6th